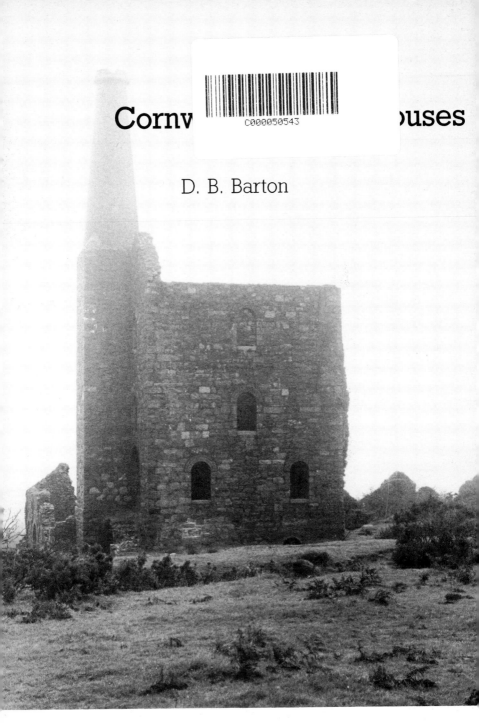

Cornwall's Engine Houses

D. B. Barton

Tor Mark Press · Penryn

This edition first published 1989 by
Tor Mark Press, Islington Wharf,
Penryn, Cornwall TR10 8AT

ISBN 0-85025-312-8

Acknowledgements
The text of this edition is based on *The Story of Cornwall's Engine Houses* and
has been edited by J.A. Buckley. The photographs in this edition were taken
specially for this edition by Paul White, except those on pages 10, 12, 16 and
17 which are reproduced by kind permission of the Royal Institution of
Cornwall. The Publishers would like to express their gratitude to the Curator,
Roger Penhallurick, for his assistance in picture research.

Printed in England by Swannack, Brown & Co Ltd, Hull

*The cover photograph shows the restored 30" whim engine house at East
Pool, now in the care of the National Trust and open to the public
(SW 672415)*

*The title page shows the Prince of Wales shaft of Phoenix United on
Bodmin Moor (SX 266720)*

*Wheal Peevor, just north of Redruth, with three surviving engine houses
— from left to right a stamps engine, pumping engine and whim (OS grid
reference SW 705442)*

Wheal Unity Wood, a rich copper and tin mine latterly worked under the names West Poldice and Tollgullow United (SW 736436). The 70″ pumping engine from here went to Tincroft Mine where it was scrapped about 1940

Scattered about the countryside throughout much of west Cornwall one sees tall gaunt ruined buildings which are unlike any to be seen elsewhere in Britain, most resembling perhaps ancient Irish castles except where they are accompanied by the sentinel presence of a stack. Dotted here and there across the landscape, either singly or in groups of two or three, and visible for many miles, these are the engine-houses that mark the sites of mines active in former days. In most cases these silent derelict buildings are the last remains of the nineteenth century tin and copper mines for which Cornwall was once justly famous. They are enduring monuments to the county in the day when mining here was of the first importance and Cornwall was a name reckoned amongst the foremost in the whole mining world. There are in fact more engine-houses and other nineteenth century mining remains here in the far south-western corner of England than anywhere else in the world.

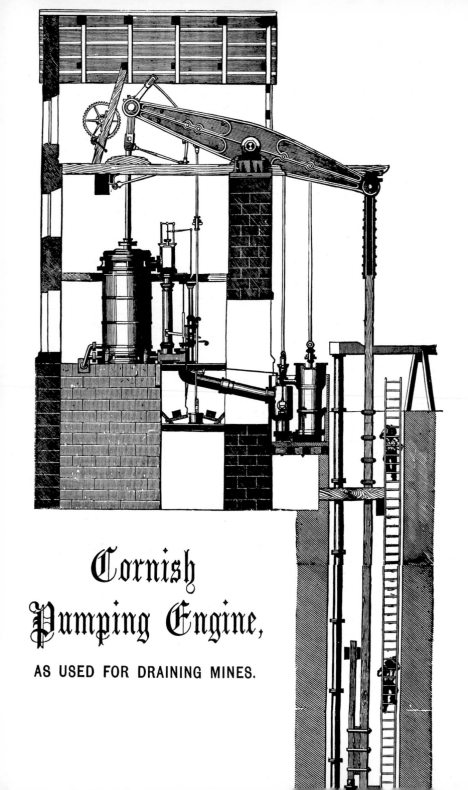

Cornish Pumping Engine,

AS USED FOR DRAINING MINES.

Although there are differing sizes and styles of these buildings, now in varying states of repair, all served a common purpose — to house the steam engines with which the mine was worked. First and foremost were the pumping engines which kept mines drained. On a big deep mine, to cope with this gargantuan task in Cornwall's wet winters, there were gargantuan engines. Steam cylinders five or six feet in diameter were commonplace; others were more than seven feet and a few ran to no less that 100″ — inches and not feet being the way in which Cornish engineers measured their engines. These dimensions may be compared to the 24″ or so cylinders of an express locomotive in the days of steam, although it is true that the latter used steam at a far higher pressure than did the old Cornish engines.

These pumping engines in Cornwall all shared the same principal features, being beam engines which transmitted the immense slow power of the piston rod to the pump rod in the shaft by means of a vast beam (or rocking lever, as Americans would term it) overhead. This great lever, at first made of wood but later almost always two massive pieces of cast iron, might weigh over fifty tons in the case of a big engine. In Cornwall, which had its own distinctive nomenclature, this beam was known as the bob. It rested on the bob wall, at the front of the house, which had to be the thickest and strongest part of the structure to withstand the stresses of its movement. At the outer (or out-door) end of the bob, the topmost of the pump rods was fastened. A long column of these wooden rods descended into the shaft, which lay beneath the 'nose' of the bob. The pumps after 1800 were of the plunger type, raising water in a series of 'lifts', or stages, successively. The weight of the descending rods alone worked these pumps, not the steam stroke of the engine which merely lifted the line of rods up again for the next stroke. Underground there were massive balance bobs (beams) added to the rods to enable this weight to be adjusted both for smooth working and for differing loads as a mine deepened.

A typical mine might be 150 fathoms deep (900′) and in the engine (or pumping) shaft would be the line of timber rods, each about 60′, or 70′ long, reaching to this depth. The 'rising main' up which the water was raised by the action of the descending plungers in each lift of pumps was of cast-iron, bolted together in lengths usually of about 6′. Their diameter might be as little as 6″, or as much as 20″, depending on the amount of water coming into the mine. The line of massive rods, the beam, the steam cylinder and thus the whole size of the engine and its house was in proportion to its designed task. A

Opposite: from an advertisement by Harveys Foundry, Hayle, 1884, "showing the usual method for the unwatering of deep mines". The engine house is shown in cross-section, and the central role of the bob wall is clearly seen

typical big engine might be a 90″, with 45 ton beam, working a 200 fathoms deep line of rods 12″ square (more at surface, less as the depth increased and thus the working load decreased) and raising water through 15″ bore pumps; at the other end of the scale, a small 36″ engine might be coupled to a 12 ton beam, 6″ rods and pumps, operating to only 50 fathoms depth.

It was not only the extent and depth of a mine that made the difference in pumping requirements. Some parts of Cornwall were wetter than others; granite for instance is much 'drier' than is clay-slate. Pumping was heavier in winter than in summer, for it is primarily upon rainfall that the amount of underground water depends; if the winter was unusually wet, with prolonged periods of rain, engines had to be speeded up. One that normally worked at a leisurely 5 strokes per minute, as was about the average, might have to be accelerated (by adjustment of the 'cataract' — a form of governor) up to 8 strokes to keep the water from rising in the mine. In emergencies and exceptional cases an engine might have to be well and truly flogged, working for weeks at 10, 12 or even 14 strokes a minute as was known even with ponderous engines such as those of 80″ and 90″ cylinder. Usually in such cases the limiting factor was the pitwork within the shaft, which might not stand up to such a rate of working, breaking long before the engine itself.

In relatively few cases did a pumping engine raise the mine water to the surface. Usually a drainage level or adit had been driven underground early in the mine's life to enable water to be drained away naturally by gravity, usually into the nearest valley. Thus it was the depth of a mine below adit that mattered for pumping purposes, although in some cases water might be raised to surface in a smaller quantity for tin dressing or other purposes on the mine.

These then were the pumping engines which occupied the majority of the engine-houses that we see today; less numerous were the winding engines or whims which were contained within smaller but basically similar structures. These whims were more or less identical machines, but smaller and less powerful, being used to haul ore or waste rock — 'deads' as a Cornish miner would say — out of a mine. The engine itself, comprising valve gear, cylinder, steam case and bob, was like a small pumping engine as far as the nose of the bob. There, instead of being fastened to a line of pump rods, it was coupled to a connecting (or sweep rod) and by that to a crank on an axle.

Opposite: Wheal Coates (SW 699500) seen from Chapel Porth. Mines on the cliffs generally had an adit flowing out to the beach; here the adit can be seen at low tide. The mine buildings are surrounded by medieval and later open workings

Levant Mine, Pendeen, produced an enormous output of copper, tin and arsenic. The small whim engine house on the left is in the care of the National Trust and contains a 30" engine built by Harveys of Hayle in 1840. The roofless building contained a 40" (later 45") pumping engine and the top of Engine Shaft is visible between them (SW 369346)

On the opposite page is the Higher Bal Shaft at Levant, which was worked for copper from the 1820s till the 1920s and for tin also after 1852 (SW 371341)

The axle carried a flywheel and winding drum over which the chain was wound. The standard flywheel was distinctive; a large diameter casting with gracefully thin rim and spokes, quite unlike the usual conception of a ponderous flywheel. This was the type known as a rotative beam engine and was to be found on most sizeable Cornish mines after about 1850. They had been in use since the late eighteenth century but were not widespread. The major mines had two, three or even more, whilst those that were still shallow or in the development stages had to rely upon the older standby of a horsewhim, in which a pair of horses turned the winding drum by a contraption not unlike a giant overhead capstan. The usual cylinder diameter of a steam whim in Cornwall was about 28″, though varying from 18″ in some cases to 30″ in others, depending on the depth of the mine.

The mode of winding ore was primitive by colliery standards of the day, for most Cornish shafts were small by comparison with collieries and were seldom vertical throughout their full depth. As a result hauling speeds were low and the loads carried very light. Kibbles, or iron buckets, were used at first, egg-shaped in order to lessen the chances of a snag (or hitch) on the roughly hewn rock sides of the shaft; skips came into use after about 1870, running up and down a primitive form of road between a frame made of timber. These were both safer and faster, but with horse-whims the old fashioned kibble continued in use in a very few cases until well into this century. Even with the bigger steam whims separate haulage shafts for raising ore were rare; usually part of the main engine or pumping shaft was utilised for this. Some engines were arranged to wind from more than one shaft, the rope being carried from drum to shaft along a series of pulleys carried on stands and making, in some cases, a few turns on the way. Most whim engine-houses were sited near the working shaft, placed at right angles to the larger house immediately beside the shaft where the pumping engine was installed. Exceptionally a whim engine might be sited behind the pumping engine house, due to the exigencies of the mine's situation — perhaps on a hillside or a cliff slope — in which case the rope passed over the main house to the pulley on the headgear above the shaft. But this meant that the whim driver could not see his kibble come up to surface and had to rely either on the indifferent help of a primitive indicator beside his engine — usually a wooden peg moving up or down a miniature version of the shaft against the engine-house wall — or even more likely the swift shout or signal bell from the lander. Accidents as a result of over-winding were not numerous, however, as they would have been in colliery working, for Cornish whims were well known for their slow rope speed.

Rotative beam engines similar to whims were also used to provide power for various other purposes on a big mine. Man engines — a form of moving ladder for raising men to surface, not unlike a line of pump rods — were one, while ore-crushers and steam capstans were also used. But stamps engines were the principal type other than whims, used for driving machinery for stamping vein rock as the first stage in preparing it for the smelter. This had not been necessary on copper mines where it was the ore itself rather than a metal concentrate which was sold by the mine; but after about 1870 batteries of stamps had become essential on all the major tin mines to crush ore raised to surface. These stamps might be likened to immense pestles-and-mortars, with cast-iron head lifting and falling in blow after blow onto the ore being fed to it on a perforated surface below. The steam engine provided power to turn the long axle from which projections engaged to lift the stamp heads one after the other. As

A battery of Cornish stamps at Levant about 1900. Stamps are first mentioned in Cornwall in 1493. Steam power replaced water-power by the early nineteenth century

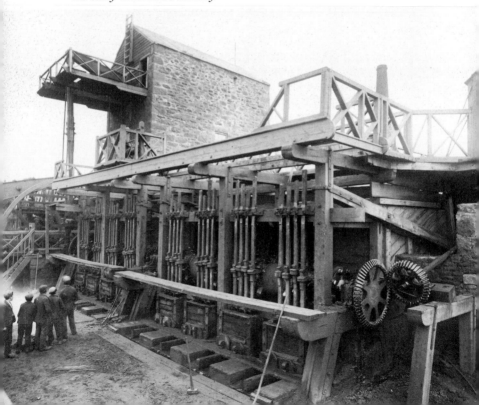

Robinson's engine, South Crofty (SW 667413). The engine house has clearly been modified for a more recent engine and winding gear

many as 48 or 64 stamps — exceptionally even 128 — might be worked by one such engine, usually of about 28″ cylinder size. The site of an old set of these steam stamps (smaller water-wheel operated sets of stamps were also used widely) can usually be distinguished fairly readily: traces of the foundations extend to one side or sometimes to both, ahead of the house. By it too (and usually on a slope below) will be the remains of the former dressing floors where the rest of the tin dressing operations were carried on.

Ventonwyn, west of St Austell (SW 963504) stands in the middle of a field: this engine house once contained a 36" engine for pumping and stamps

Opposite: Wheal Trewavas (SW 600265), less well known than Botallack near Land's End but just as dramatic, was a copper mine which was worked under the sea and was closed by flooding. During the Tributors' annual undersea celebratory dinner, water began to drip on the diners, who barely escaped! The lower engine (Old Shaft) was an 18", the higher (New Shaft) was a 45" Harvey

It is easy to forget, when we see just a surviving engine house, what a destructive effect mining had on the landscape. This is the Tuckingmill valley of the Red River as it was in the 1890s, looking north from the railway, approximately from SW 663407; many of the buildings including the chapel are still there

The dressing floors in the foreground are just downstream from Dolcoath which was to the left of the camera. Old Cook's Kitchen Mine is behind the camerman's right shoulder; the engine house on the skyline to the left is North Roskear and the chimneys to the right are an arsenic works. In the 1870s there were up to 40 stream-works on the Red River

Most of the engine-houses seen today are at least a century old, and if they are not disturbed by the hand of man will last as long again, perhaps much longer. This longevity is due to the inherently massive construction, for the largest available blocks of stone were used. The engineers were building with an eye not to longevity but to the fact that the house — to the foundations of which the engine was fastened down — had to weigh more than the loads imposed by pumping. The cylinder was anchored down to the bedstones, immense slabs of granite bolted to their fellows to form a solid core to the foundations; the bob rested on the heavy wall which was of particularly massive construction and made of stone specially selected by the masons.

The outer walls were little less substantial and the windows were kept to as small a size as possible to avoid weakening the structure at all. A typical large house, built on Tresavean Mine near Redruth in 1840 for an 85″ engine, weighed 2400 tons inclusive of the materials used for the stack and boilerhouse. Weight and strength were also essential for absorbing any vibration from the working of the engine or any jarring from a sudden fluctuation in load. The house in fact was regarded as part of the engine and had to be designed and built accordingly. The engineer who was responsible for the engine also drew up plans for the house. Wherever possible he would specify granite for the bob wall, to withstand crushing. In 'killas' or clay slate areas this wall alone might be built of granite and the rest of locally raised stone but for a first-rate engine blocks of granite would be used throughout for strength. In some cases other engine-houses — sometimes quite distant ones — were pulled down to provide suitable stone for a new house being built.

Beside every engine-house stood the lower, single-storey building which contained the boiler or boilers used for providing steam for the engine. A small pumping engine, whim or stamps usually had a single one; big pumping engines as many as five or six. Occasionally boiler-houses were separate structures but in the case of whim engines or small pumping engines a lean-to structure against the main house served for the single boiler required.

Many of these boiler-houses have today disappeared from the scene, largely because they were of normal building construction and have

Opposite: Great Wheal Busy near Chacewater (SW 738448); the principal engine house, built in the 1850s and with boiler house still intact today, contained at different periods 80″, 90″ and 85″ engines, the last of which was broken up in 1952. This mine worked intermittently from the late seventeenth century until 1920

Wheal Kitty, St Agnes (SW 724513)

thus been demolished or rifled in subsequent years as a source of building stone. Their slate roofs have invariably gone, as have most of those on engine-houses despite their inaccessible height, in many cases to provide a replacement for the thatch on some nearby cottage or two.

Serving the boiler-house, be it large or small, was a substantial stack or chimney, usually built into the corner of the engine-house for strength (plus the added weight it gave to the structure) but sometimes free standing. Almost invariably these were circular in section, with very few of the square-section stacks common in most colliery districts elsewhere in Britain. Local stone was used up to about two-thirds of the height, with the remainder of brick. In a few cases this composite construction was due to a subsequent increase in height of the stack in an attempt to get better combustion from the poor quality coal that latter-day Cornish mines were driven to use as an economy measure, but in the majority it was simply that this made for the easiest and most economic construction. Masonry was cheaper for the more substantial lower part, whilst bricks, although much dearer, were more manageable to raise to the considerable height involved — up primitive wooden scaffolding one should remember — as well as being better suited to the thinner walling requisite at the top of a tapering stack. Some extremely graceful and well proportioned stacks are still to be seen up and down the county, with brickwork which has lasted as a testimonial to the men who laid it a century ago.

Hawkes engine house at Killifreth Mine, between Scorrier and Chacewater, has one of the tallest, and certainly the most graceful, of surviving stacks (SW 734442). The house was built in 1892 for an 80" engine which broke up in 1897 and was replaced in 1914 with an 85"; the chimney was then increased to its present height

Tregurtha Downs, near Marazion (SW 538310)

Lightning has been one of the great destroyers of engine-house stacks over the years, and this was also a hazard to which they, and engine-houses, were exposed throughout their working lives particularly those in exposed places. Various cases of damage to them up and down the county are on record, with the damage in some cases even extending to the engine itself within. A more common danger was fire, and very many cases are on record of gutted engine-houses. The presence of bone-dry timbers in the various floors and staircases, plus a great deal of oil and tallow used in lubrication, made engine-houses more vulnerable in this respect than might be supposed. In the big engine-house remaining at Tregurtha Downs Mine near Marazion, now converted to a house, there was for example a fire which burned for the whole of one day in January 1889. Fire such as this in the vital centre of a mine's operations meant the end of pumping for a time and might in some cases result in the closing down of a mine for ever. To guard against this possibility a few houses were even intended to be of fireproof construction. Iron was used for staircases, flooring and roof beams, with slate slabs for the floor itself, thus eliminating almost all woodwork.

Being massively built, engines usually withstood the heat and even the collapse of floors and roof onto them, surprisingly well. Far more damaging was any accident to the pitwork in the shaft. It will be appreciated that a breakage of the main rod and the consequent sudden loss of load could have disastrous effects upon the engine. It might displace the beam, smash the piston and split the cylinder. In a bad smash the piston rod, 8″ or 9″ in diameter, might even be bent in two as though it were a knitting needle. For this reason the pitwork was tended carefully in all well-run mines to guard against such breakages, whilst big wooden safety blocks were bolted within the house to cushion some of the blow in minor cases.

Another hazard was the possibility of the main beam breaking, an eventuality which again could wreck an engine. Moreover if the outdoor half fell into the shaft, as was always possible, irreparable damage might be done to the mine as a working entity. After the Hartley colliery disaster in Durham in 1862, when 204 miners were trapped and killed as a result of just such an occurrence which blocked the means of entry and exit to the workings, bobs were inspected carefully, whilst replacements or new designs thereafter incorporated more massive beams of wider section. Cast iron, however, continued in widespread use in Cornwall despite its inherent unsuitability in this respect.

Most large engine-houses were built on three floors: the ground floor (which actually was above ground level on account of the partly raised foundation or 'loading' to which the cylinder was bolted down); the middle chamber, more or less at the height of the top of the cylinder; and the top floor or bob loft, which was on a level with the bob. From this the engine-man could walk out through the doors in the weather-boarded topmost portion above the bob-wall, onto the bob 'plat'. There he could inspect the bob and could see the shaft below. Some smaller engines were erected in houses with only two floors but this was relatively rare, and gave a cramped layout within the house which was unpopular with engine-men.

Under normal conditions, pumping engines virtually ran themselves for hours on end, indeed almost for days, without the need for any control or adjustment. With hard pressed over-loaded engines coupled to ancient pitwork, it was a very different matter but a well run engine required so little attention that drivers — as engine-men were always called in Cornwall — had one of the most leisurely jobs anywhere on the mine. They were, however, expected to do their own stoking, although with assistance where a large engine had several boilers supplying steam. Whim engines were different of course, requiring to be started, stopped and reversed for each load of ore. Stamps engines required somewhat less attention, running for very long periods at a stretch without the necessity for stopping.

Whim Engine, with Winding Cage attached.

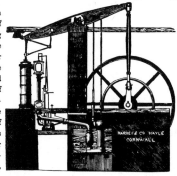

The accompanying Illustration represents a side elevation of a Whim Engine with Winding Cage attached. This is the ordinary Engine employed for raising the productions of the Mine, and is sometimes adapted for the threefold purposes of Winding, Crushing, and Pumping. These Engines are made in the best modern style and of any power required. Estimates for simple Winding Engines, for Engines adapted to other purposes, with pump, gearing, straps, and boilers complete, furnished on application. These Engines are well finished and made in the most approved style and of any power required. For Winding it is only necessary to state the height and daily tonnage of the lift. If for Crushing, state the number of tons and description of material required to be crushed in a given time ; and if for Pumping, the depth of mine and quantity of water (in gallons) to be raised per hour.

—:o:—

ESTIMATES, DESIGNS, AND ALL INFORMATION GIVEN ON APPLICATION.

An advertisement by Harveys of Hayle, for a whim engine

This engine house at Hingston Down, near Gunnislake, is unusual because the roof is hidden by a parapet. One engine was used for both winding and pumping. The mine was worked in Victorian times for copper, and in Edwardian times for tin, arsenic, copper and wolfram (SX 408715)

South Tincroft near Carn Brea; this horizontal house held not a pumping engine but an air compressor to power rock drills, from about 1890 to 1921 (SW 668406)

The standard exterior finish of an engine-house in the nineteenth century heyday of mining was white-wash, with red paint for all exposed woodwork — a striking combination which contrasts strongly with the natural stone-work that we now automatically attribute to these buildings. Inside, all houses were reputed to be kept spotless; the walls painted or varnished, as was the steam case; the floors scrubbed almost to a degree of whiteness; the settle where the driver rested or ate his 'croust' spick and span, whilst curtains or even potted geraniums might grace the windows and sills. Warm and comfortable the engine-house might be, but miners and surface workers were never found there. They were, however, permitted into the boiler-house in the days before proper 'drys' were provided for the miners to change in and this became the usual place for them to leave their underground working clothes to dry between cores. Boiler explosions were an all too common feature on the mines due to inadequate safety regulations prior to the 1870s and the deaths of miners and others congregated in these improvised 'drys' occurred on several occasions from this cause.

These two much photographed engine houses are on the Crowns section of Botallack mine (named after the nearby rocks); the lower house held a pumping engine and the upper a winding engine for the famous Diagonal Shaft beneath the sea (SW 363336)

Opposite: West Kitty, Thomas' Shaft, directly behind houses on the B3277 into St Agnes (SW 719504); its 40" engine is now preserved at the Science Museum, London

Below: East Wheal Rose, now on the site of the Lappa Valley Railway, was Cornwall's most productive lead and silver mine (SW 838558) and the engine house once contained a massive 100" pumping engine

Above: South Polgooth, a small late nineteenth century mine (SX 989498)

Above left: Polberro, overlooking St Agnes (SW 717514) and in surprisingly good repair, contained a 60" engine. This was an important tin mine in the mid-nineteenth century, and was worked again in the twentieth

East Kit Hill Mine, beside the A390 (SX 389711) is one of the easiest engine houses to spot as one enters the county; it was a small tin producer from 1853-1909

Wheal Agar, Taylor's Shaft, preserved with a 90" pumping engine; EPAL stands for East Pool and Agar Ltd (SW 674419). The bob wall is 80" thick to support the massive double bob, 32' long and weighing 52 tons, which pumped from 1700' depth

Rogers Shaft of East Wheal Lovell, a familiar landmark on the Helston to Falmouth road (SW 699314)

United Downs was one of the most extensive copper mines, with over 80 miles of underground workings and perhaps twenty steam engines. Little remains except this stamp engine house (SW 748416)

The number of engines at work in Cornwall was at its peak in the 1860s when over 600 pumping engines, whims or stamps might then have been counted. Many of the houses we now see remaining are from this era, and are thus more than a century old. There are others of later period, well into the twentieth century, but very few of earlier date. Part of a structure may well be so, for some of the nineteenth century engines stood beside shafts where atmospheric Newcomen engines had worked in the eighteenth century, but the houses were usually rebuilt, in part or in whole, when a new engine was installed.

Wheal Jenkin, Bellingham's Shaft, lurking in the mists of Caradon Hill (SX 265715)

In a number of cases the houses we see, particularly those on old and historic mines, have held a succession of different engines. The intermittent nature of mine working in Cornwall, more or less corresponding to the ups and downs of the price of metal over the decades, meant that the same engine-house might contain three or even four different engines in half a century. From similar causes, the movement of engines from mine to mine — as one closed down and another opened up elswhere — was a constant feature. A brisk and continuing trade in second, third and even fourth-hand engines was carried on, ranging in size and type from the smallest of whims to the biggest of the ones used for pumping. Cornish engineers thought little of the task of taking down the most massive of engines, moving it across half the county over appalling or almost non-existent roads, and re-erecting it on a new site.

After the decline of copper mining in the 1860s and of tin in the decade or so after that, the number of engines at work in the county dwindled rapidly. Many were broken up for scrap, sometimes after years of being abandoned where they stood, whilst others were shipped off to collieries or other mines in Britain and countries abroad. A few of the smaller ones found a last home on china-clay works in the St. Austell district. The last beam engine to work on a mine in the county was a venerable 80″ at South Crofty Mine which ceased work in May 1955. This engine is still in existence and was preserved by the Cornish Engines Preservation Society, being now in the care of the National Trust. Two other surviving engines, a 30″ whim and a 90″ pumping engine, are similarly preserved for posterity on the site of the former East Pool Mine near Redruth. They can be visited by the public in the summer months and are notable relics (as can be seen on the cover of this book) of Cornwall's great mining past in the days of steam.